RELIGIONS AND CULTURES

A guide to beliefs, customs and diversity for Health and Social Care Services.

Sixth Edition

DR MOUSSA JOGEE O.B.E.

RELIGIONS AND CULTURES

A guide to beliefs, customs and diversity for health and social care services.

Sixth Edition

Published by
R&C Publications
PO Box 14330
Burntisland KY3 9WU
Tel/Fax: 01592 871291
www.religionsandcultures.co.uk
enquiries@religionsandcultures.co.uk

To order copies please contact the publisher at the above address

The contents of this booklet have been compiled and published in good faith and the publisher accepts no liability for any claim arising from them whether the loss is direct or indirect

ISBN-10: 0954757904
ISBN-13: 978-0-9547579-0-8

CONTENTS

ABOUT THE EDITOR

Moussa Jogee spent a lifetime working for equality. He was born in 1930 in South Africa and educated in India, before returning to South Africa where he was active in the struggle against apartheid. Granted political asylum in the UK in 1965, Moussa continued his work in equality, becoming involved in the Campaign Against Racial Discrimination, Lothian Community Relations Council, and Lothian Race Equality Council. In 1994 he was appointed to the Commission for Racial Equality (CRE) as Commissioner with Special Responsibility for Scottish Affairs, and subsequently as Deputy Chair of the CRE until his retirement in 2002.

ACKNOWLEDGEMENTS

Thanks must be recorded to all those who helped in the production of this and all previous editions. In particular, we would like to record our special thanks to Glenda Watt, Farid Jiwa, Dr N Shah, Ben Yuen, John Macintyre, Jody Higgs, B.M. Mody, Hafizur Rahman, Suraksha Vohra, Graham Barnes, Rev T Stewart Mc Gregor, K Allen, David Kreikneir-Watson, and Inderjit-Singh.

Special thanks go to my colleague Saroj Lal for her assistance in the production and distribution of earlier editions of this booklet, during her time as Senior Community Relations Officer at the Lothian Community Relations Council and subsequently as director of the Lothian Race Equality Council.

While I am grateful for all this help and encouragement, any errors in this guide are my sole responsibility.

EDITORS NOTE

The purpose of this guide is to raise awareness, promote understanding, and to provide practical, operational information about the needs of ethnic minority community members in our institutional care. Rather than claiming to exhaustively provide all the answers, it outlines beliefs, customs, practices and rules pertinent to particular communities. As with majority communities, custom and practice vary widely. For example, some Muslim girls will cover their heads, others will not. Some Buddhists will eat meat, others will not. This diversity guide seeks only to draw its readers' attention to some salient points relevant to their work practices. Assumption cannot be relied on – always ask what practice is preferred.

In a brief guidebook such as this, it is impossible to cover all types of belief and practice, both formal and informal, followed by all cultural and religious groups in the UK. However this guide aims to provide basic information about the main religious and community groups.

INTRODUCTION TO THE SIXTH EDITION

Britain is now a richly diverse multi-cultural and multi-faith society. There are immigrant communities who have been resident here for decades and there are ethnic groups who have arrived only recently. But for all of these, whether born here or recent incomers, customs and practices, religious and otherwise, are often passed on from one generation to the next. In the interest of sympathetic understanding, this booklet has been prepared as a basic guide to information about beliefs and customs for Schools and for Health, Prison, Social Services and other caring organisations to ensure that our institutional services reflect the needs of all the communities in Britain.

This booklet contains two sections – a short good practice guide to providing culturally aware care and a more detailed look at such different ethnic groups and faiths as Baha'is, Buddhists, Chinese, Hindus, Jews, Muslims, Sikhs, Rastafarians and Zoroastrians. Each chapter gives a short general introduction and information on such matters as birth and death and associated practices, family planning, notions of modesty and perceptions of medical and social services, as well as assumptions concerning illness itself.

This sixth edition has been prepared in consultation with UK religious and cultural groups and their related organisations; and where relevant, with health and other professionals. In addition to new information on language, names, community sizes and national contact listings, the contents and format of this guide have been fully revised, edited and updated.

Dr Moussa Jogee OBE

Published by
R & C Publications, PO Box 14330, Burntisland KY3 9WU
Tel/Fax: 01592 871291
web: www.religionsandcultures.co.uk
E-Mail: enquiries@religionsandcultures.co.uk

GENERAL GUIDELINES

This section gives a general guide to good practice and a summary of how to provide a culturally aware service.

General

- Establish ethnic identity and religious affiliation of the patient or person receiving care and note this information in case notes.
- Talk to the patient, their friends and family, community leaders or consult guides for more information and advice

Diet

Religious limitation of diet, and food preferences generally, are very important considerations when caring for, or dealing with, many ethnic minorities. There are foodstuffs that are forbidden, others that must be prepared in a particular manner, some which must not be combined in the same meal, fasting periods that must be observed, as well as preferences that should be accommodated wherever possible.

- A few vegetarian choices on the daily menu would go a long way towards meeting the needs of all the groups mentioned in this booklet if a specific meal is not available for them.
- Vegetarian means not only no meat but also no butter, cheese and eggs. Many groups will also not eat fish. Fruit is always an acceptable option.
- Some may find hospital food bland compared with their usual diet.
- Take care to avoid cross contamination. Do not transfer serving utensils from one bowl or dish to another. Those used for serving 'forbidden' food must not be used for serving other foods.
- If permitted, consider allowing family, friends or community to bring in food for a patient as this is often more acceptable.
- Do not put milk into drinks automatically; for example, many Jews will not accept milk mixed with other liquids.
- Try to keep the names of dishes simple and descriptive. For example, people may not understand what is in 'Irish stew'.

The Vegetarian Society is willing to assist hospital-catering departments, and will send a set of basic free literature on request (enclose 2nd class postage stamp). The address is: The Vegetarian Centre, 53 Marloes Road, Kensington, London W8 6LD.

Language

Although command of English among members of minority ethnic communities born in Britain is the same as for the rest of the population, only around half of those born abroad may be fully literate in any language. This can lead to differences in language that can hamper communication between staff and those in their care.

- Always ask patients about their preferred language
- If you do not have the appropriate resources, make full use of translation and interpretation services. It is not appropriate to use family members to translate.
- Even those with a good grasp of English may not understand medical or legal terms. Keep your language simple, and explain terms as you go.
- Do not patronise an individual who is having difficulty under-standing or expressing themselves by speaking loudly or rudely.
- Make sure the person in care has actually understood what you have said. Ask them to ask you questions if anything is unclear or ask them to repeat a diagnosis.
- Use all available professionally translated resources to help you

Names

Most people in this country are accustomed to identifying themselves by their 'given' (or 'Christian') names followed by their surnames, and to being indexed according to their surname. This is not a universal practice, and confusion may arise when recording the names of some ethnic minorities. Probably the best policy is to ask the patient for his or her family name and most used personal name, and use the family name as 'surname' for recording purposes. Examples are given in the appropriate sections of different faiths in the booklet.

- Having decided which name will be used as the 'surname', it should be made clear that this is the name by which the individual will be known in the records from then on.
- If you are unsure how to spell a name, then ask them to write it out for you on a card, to ensure that it is spelt correctly in their records.
- Many ethnic groups do not give their child a permanent name for some time after birth. It is important to make a note of any temporary names and amend records when a child receives a permanent name.

Notions of Modesty

Many cultures and groups have rules about the clothing they should wear and which areas of the body should be covered up. Likewise many cultures have a taboo against certain behaviours such as being touched or touching members of the opposite sex or people they do not know.

- Patients of all cultures may feel exposed in back-opening hospital gowns. Allow patients to cover up with dressing gowns to help them to feel more secure.

- Ritual items of clothing such as a Sikh's turban or a marriage bangle must be properly respected and cared for if have to be removed from the individual. Put them into a container and keep safe. Never place directly onto the floor.

- People of many cultures (especially, but not only, women) will not expose any more of their body than they need to. Unless unavoidable, do not ask for the removal of items of clothing, head coverings, ritual items, jewellery, make-up or personal items as this may cause real distress.

- If in consultation with a man, women may often feel more comfortable with a chaperone in the room. In some cultures, women are not meant to look directly into the eyes of an unknown man.

- Many people prefer to wash themselves in running water, so showers should be made available where possible. If this is not possible, a basin and a supply of fresh water must be offered. Many faiths perform ablutions before prayer. Access to a suitable area should be provided.

- After using a lavatory some people prefer to wash with water rather than using toilet paper, which they consider unhygienic. Make sure some water is provided for this.

- In many cultures, men and women are strictly segregated. This may have implications for many forms of care, particularly healthcare, in relation to admission onto a mixed ward and physical examinations being carried out by staff of the opposite gender.

- Where possible, arrange for women to be treated by women and admitted to all-female wards; similar consideration should be shown to men.

- Children and women may feel more comfortable being treated if they have a chaperone with them. This would often be a close family member.

Death

Customs in death vary widely from culture to culture. Issues such as the use of life support, organ donation, post mortems as well as dealing with death, mourning and ceremony differ from person to person and culture to culture. Advice should therefore be sought at all stages to ensure that cultural requirements are adhered to with sensitivity. There are, however, a number of guidelines that will help in dealing with a death situation.

- Where possible, discuss with a dying patient's family any requirements they may have for the process of death - for example, facing the bed towards Mecca or having prayers said.

- Many people may not want to know if they are dying, or may not want their families to know. Discuss this with the patient, or ask to talk to their community leader, a chaplain, etc.

- Do not remove items associated with the faith or culture of the deceased after their death. The family may wish to do this themselves.

- Preserve dignity and modesty at all times. Keep a body covered with a clean, white cloth.

- Some communities do not like to have their dead handled by people from outside the group. Do not touch the body directly unless unavoidable, but use gloves instead. Likewise do not wash the body. Family and friends may wish to do this themselves as a last mark of respect for their dead.

- Some cultures require a speedy burial or cremation and the remains of their dead may be gathered quickly for this purpose. If the deceased was not born in the UK, the body may need to be quickly released for transportation to their home country before burial.

- If law requires a post-mortem, then explain this gently to relatives, who may be distressed by this.

- Mourning traditions vary considerably. It is important to offer the family and friends a quiet nearby room to congregate in.

National Contacts

It is important to note that not all religions or community groups have a single, structured national representative organisation. However the contact details given at the end of each section denote the most appropriate representative body at a UK level for any readers to address their further enquiries to in the first instance.

BAHA'IS

'The earth is but one country and mankind its citizens.' *(Baha'u'llah)*
Estimated Community Size: Global 7,100,000 : UK 6,000

History, Beliefs and Principles

The name of the founder of the Baha'i Faith is Baha'ullah (Glory of God). The faith originated in Persia in the middle of the nineteenth century. Baha'ullah was persecuted and finally exiled by the authorities to Akka (Acre) in Palestine where he passed away in 1892. The spiritual and administrative centre of the faith is thus the Holy Land.

Baha'is believe in the one God who reveals His purpose progressively throughout human history. They believe our current stage in history is characterised by issues of global interdependence and Baha'ullah teaches that humankind must follow the principle of the "oneness of mankind". This recognises that while people are diverse in their aims, aspirations and cultures, it is imperative that they work co-operatively in a spirit of "unity".

The Baha'is Faith is an independent world religion with laws and ordinances. Baha'is have a great respect for physicians and are exhorted to consult the best possible medical advice when ill.

Baha'is have a great respect for life. Each person has a soul that comes into being at conception. During a person's lifetime, the soul acquires the spiritual attributes required for the next stage of existence, which occurs after death.

Predominant Languages

Baha'is are found in all continents and they come from many nationalities and cultures. Therefore there is no one predominant language, and most in the UK pray and read scriptures in English. However as the faith originated in Persia, some may use Persian (Farsi) and Arabic.

Worship

The Baha'is have no fixed worship services and no ordained priesthood or clergy. However Baha'is are required to say an obligatory prayer each day and to read from the Holy Scriptures of the faith each morning and evening. When praying, Baha'is turn in the direction of Bahji, near Akka in Israel. During illness, they are exempted from obligatory prayer.

Diet

Baha'is have no dietary prohibitions. Some Baha'is may be vegetarian but this is their own choice and not a religious requirement. The use of alcohol and habit-forming drugs is strictly prohibited except when prescribed by a physician. Smoking is discouraged.

Fasting

Fasting takes place on the 19 days from the 2nd to the 20th March. This is a time of spiritual regeneration and during the hours from sunrise to sunset each day, Baha'is may not take food or drink. Fasting is not obligatory during sickness, pregnancy, and menstruation nor for mothers who are breast-feeding and people under the age of 15 or over 70.

Birth Customs

The birth of a child is a time of joy and Baha'is may wish to express their gratitude to God with brief prayer. There are however, no rituals associated with birth.

Death Customs

Baha'is treat the body of a deceased person with great respect as it has been, during life, the vehicle of the soul. Baha'I Law prescribes that burial should take place at a distance of not more than one hour's journey from the place of death. The body should not be cremated nor embalmed. Further clarification in individual cases may be sought from the Spiritual Assembly of the Baha'is (the Baha'i administrative body) in the locality (see telephone directory). Funerals are normally arranged by the family of the deceased if available, or on occasions, by the Spiritual Assembly.

Baha'is relatives or friends will wish to say prayers for the dead.

Attitude to Medical and Social Services Staff and Illness

Baha'is have a great respect for scientifically based medical opinion and they are encouraged to seek out and to comply with the best advice. As well as taking prescribed medication, they also believe greatly in the power of prayer in the healing process.

Blood Transfusions and Transplants

Baha'is have no objection to blood transfusions.

Baha'is may leave their bodies for scientific research or donate organs for transplantation.

Family Planning

Family planning is left to personal conscience of the Baha'i but the following considerations should be born in mind.

Sterilisation in either sex is strongly discouraged. Where a medical condition is relevant to the decision, the individual should seek qualified advice.

Methods of contraception that prevent implantation of the fertilised ovum are unacceptable, as Baha'is believe that the soul comes into being at conception.

Washing and Toilet

Washing, bathing and toilet present no unusual problems.

Baha'is may wish to wash before observing their daily prayer.

Ideas of Modesty

Baha'is do not object to being examined by doctors of the opposite sex.

National Contact

National Spiritual Assembly of the Baha'is of the United Kingdom
27 Rutland Gate
London
SW17 1PD
Tel: 020 7584 2566

BUDDHISTS

'Impermanent are all created things. Strive on with awareness'
(Said to be The Buddha's last words)
Estimated Community Size: Global 360,000,000 : UK 30,000 – 130,000

History, Beliefs and Principles

The Buddhist faith centres on Mahatma Gautam Shakyamuni Buddha, who lived 2,500 years ago in India, and is revered not in the sense of Buddha the God, but as an example to humanity as a way of life. Buddhists believe the essence of Buddha is within ourselves and each of us has a part of Buddha within us. If we want to become Buddha we must realise Buddahood within ourselves through prayers, purifications, retreats and virtuous conduct such as the practice of generosity. Buddhists also believe in reincarnation. Central to the Bhuddhist belief is the injunction not to cause harm to others and to help all being.

Diet

Diets vary according to the climate of the country involved. One can find both vegetarian and non-vegetarian Buddhists. The notion of non-harming is basic to Buddha's teaching. Many Buddhists regard this as non-killing for food.

Fasting

Most fasting days occur on New Moon and Full Moon days, but there are also other festival days such as Buddha's birthday, death day, his enlightenment, the first Sermon and others. On such days one is required to eat at regular times, which means that one should eat before 12 noon and not after.

Birth Customs

A Royal or very high-class baby would have special ceremonies performed for him, but there are no special ceremonies for the babies of ordinary people. It is a time for gratitude and practices of generosity; baby blessing may be performed later.

Death Customs

In Tibetan Buddhism, it was sometimes the case that a body was kept

49 days whilst special daily prayers for the deceased took place. Normally the time before committal depends on the lunar calendar and varies from 3 to 7 days. The most important thing when a Buddhist dies is that a Buddhist priest is informed as soon as possible, and he preferably should be of the same school of Buddhism as the deceased. Most Buddhists would be quite happy to give a 'who to contact' name and this might be done systematically when a patient enters the hospital.

Ideally, the body should not be moved too much before the priest arrives. When he arrives the priest may do the necessary prayers, which could take an hour or thereabouts, depending on the school. It is not always necessary for the officiating priest to recite the prayers actually in the presence of the corpse – they can be recited at a distance, in a temple for instance. Buddhists can choose whether they would prefer to be buried or cremated.

Attitude to Medical Staff and Illness

Helping people is fundamental to Buddhist ideas, and so the patient will always respect the doctor and nurses for helping him.

Blood Transfusions and Transplants

It is unlikely there will be a problem with blood transfusions. Transplants however, can be a more complex issue. As transplantation has only become available recently, opinions on what is best may vary. As the moment of clinical death is not seen as the end of the death process, removal of organs at this time may be considered unwise. This consideration may extend to include organs 'donated' by animals.

A Buddhist can choose whether he/she would prefer to be buried or cremated. Some might also be hesitant to donate their own organs as this would imply deliberately allowing harm to be caused (to the body from which the organ was to come). Others might feel the overall benefit outweighed such concerns. Each Buddhist must decide for himself or herself in a given situation what causes the least harm and promotes the most good. Autopsies are generally considered to interfere with the process of dying and hence it may be avoided.

Family Planning

Buddhists believe that the size of one's family is dictated by one's destiny, and that this should not be interfered with. Accordingly all Buddhist traditions will disapprove of any method of family planning. If a couple do resort to one, it should be a method that safeguards the normal development of the baby if conceived. All Buddhist tradition will condemn abortion. Of the two; family planning and abortion, abortion is the much greater wrong.

Washing and Toilet

There are no beliefs or practices stipulated in Buddhist scriptures. Buddhists from different parts of the world may follow various social customs in this area.

Ideas of Modesty

There are no particular points to be noted in this area.

National Contact

The Buddhist Society
58 Eccleston Square
London
SW1V 1PH
Tel: 020 7834 5858

Network of Buddhist Organisations UK
The Old Courthouse
43 Renfrew Road
London SE11 4NA
Tel: 0208 682 3442

CHINESE and VIETNAMESE

'Impermanent are all created things. Strive on with awareness'
(Said to be The Buddha's last words)

History, Beliefs and Principles

There have been Chinese people in some parts of the UK since the early 1800's. However most immigrants arrived in the 50s and 60s – this was a time of great political uncertainty in China following the Communist Revolution and traditional fishing and agriculture industries in Hong Kong and New Territories were in a state of decline. Some 80% of Chinese people in the UK originated from the former colony of Hong Kong and the New Territories.

Although amongst Vietnamese and Chinese there are a number of belief systems, from Ancestor Worship to Islam to Christianity, the most prevalent influences on the way of life and philosophy of Chinese and Vietnamese are based on three schools of thought

Buddhism – sees life as a process of birth, ageing, illness and death in which people seek enlightenment

Confucianism – an ethical system that emphasizes law and respect for rules and authority as central to making life possible

Taoism – sees life as a balance of water, fire, earth, metal and wood

Amongst the older generation, especially the women, belief in the traditional religion is still strong. In some cases, due to the growth of modern education and influences exerted by Westernisation, religious scepticism amongst most of the younger generation has increased. However, we must not ignore the fact that amongst the numerous Chinese and Vietnamese immigrants in the U.K. there is a large number who still hold on to their traditions and customs.

VIETNAMESE

During the 70's and 80's some 15-20,000 Vietnamese people came to Britain, leaving due to political and social upheaval following 30 years of national and civil war and the Chinese invasion of Feb 1979. It is estimated that up to and 80% of all Vietnamese who fled were in fact of ethnic Chinese origin.

Principal Languages

Mandarin – the standard written language (pictorial) as well as a spoken language. The sound associated with each character varies according to dialect spoken. Cantonese and Hakka are the two predominant dialects spoken by Chinese in Britain. Regardless of spoken dialect (which are not usually mutually comprehensible), all literate Chinese will be able to read Mandarin. Most Chinese from Vietnam will speak Vietnamese (a tonal language written in Latin script) and also Cantonese.

Worship

Set forms of worship are not usually used by Vietnamese or Chinese (unless belonging to a 'formal' faith such as Christianity). Altars may be set up temporarily for specific weddings or festivals.

Names

Chinese and Vietnamese names often (but not always) have three parts. Usually the family name comes first, followed by the personal names. Sometimes in the UK this is reversed so the family name comes last, with a western personal name taken before it. If in doubt, ask for the family name. Married women don't always take the husbands name.

Festivals

YUAN TAN – Chinese New Year – the first day of the first lunar month

TENG CHIEH – Lantern Festival - the first full moon of the year

TET – Vietnamese New Year

Diet

There are very definite customs of their own concerning food, its preparation, its service, and the manner in which it is eaten. The older generation hold the belief that rice is the only form of staple food which can give them energy and vitality. Thus it is not uncommon to find that Chinese patients appear to have lost their appetite during their stay in hospital, or complain about the meals served to them in the Western style. Although complaints are seldom made direct to the medical staff, the patient may indirectly request food and rice to be brought in to them by their relatives during their visits. A traditional Chinese belief relating to diet during hospitalisation concerns the consumption of soup, which has been boiled for a long time (3 hours). Many believe that the consumption of well-prepared soup will help to clear one's system and promote speedy recovery, particularly after surgical operations. Few milk or dairy products will be used. The use of fish sauce or soya sauce can help make unfamiliar foods more acceptable.

Birth Customs

When a child is born, the relatives pay visits, bringing presents such as the traditional dish "Keung chow", eggs dyed red, chicken soup, and clothing for the baby. The mother may be unwilling to go for a bath during the first few days after birth; traditionally she should rest at this time, and immersion is sometimes regarded as bad for the health. About a month after the baby's birth the baby's head may be shaved and a special meal prepared.

Death Customs

Funeral and mourning customs vary very widely, making it very difficult to speak for all. The position and wealth or poverty of the family concerned are also factors to be considered in the performances of rites. On the death of a child or infant, the burial takes place at once with no special ceremony. As for adults, the body is bathed. The custom was and still is for some to clothe the body in white or in old-fashioned Chinese clothing or the deceased's favourite clothing. Relatives and friends will wish to see the body before the coffin lid is closed.

Only Muslim Chinese will have any objection to post-mortems.

Attitudes to Medical and Social Work Staff and Illness

Due to Western influences over the last two or three decades Western medicine has become established in Hong Kong and it has been accepted by the majority of the Chinese as the most advanced form of treatment. However, there is a minority who are still accustomed to the traditional herbal remedies given by Chinese physicians when they fall ill. Most now feel it is possible to reconcile aspects of traditional and Western medicine.

Blood Transfusions and Transplants

Although Chinese and Vietnamese have no specific religious objections to these, there is frequently a great apprehension about operations of any kind and there is a wide spread dislike of giving blood samples.

Family Planning

Chinese and Vietnamese accept family planning devices and even abortion. However family planning matters should not be mentioned in the presence of other Chinese / Vietnamese and may not be a matter normally discussed openly between the sexes.

The idea of having a balance of male and female children is growing, though the preference for male descendants is still strong among more traditionally minded parents.

Ideas of Modesty

In general Chinese and Vietnamese women have a comparatively reserved and modest nature. They would probably be more contented and relaxed when they are being attended by a female professional. Reassurance and explanation by medical professionals on the various treatment procedures carried out on the patient is seen to be essential in order to gain their co-operation and trust. Fear on the part of the patient is often generated through ignorance of what is happening around him/her.

Other Special Considerations

Antibiotics

In Vietnam, a much higher dosage is prescribed. Vietnamese feel that the lower dosage prescribed here does not have the same effect.

Traditional Chinese Medicine

Chinese traditional medicine is still very prevalent amongst the community. It is broadly based upon the key concepts of yin and yang, ch'i and the five elements of matter that are described in the Taoist belief. Illness is seen as an imbalance of these elements and therefore treatment is focused on restoring balance and harmony. Many of these medicines are available in major cities in the UK.

CHRISTIANS

'I give you a new commandment; love one another; as I have loved you, so you are to love one another.' (Jesus to his disciples)

Estimated Community Size: Global 2,000,000,000 : UK 38,100,000

History, Beliefs and Principles

Christianity is still the main religion of Britain, residually affecting language, literature, values, beliefs, laws and culture. The belief that the nature and purpose of God have been revealed in the life and teachings of Jesus Christ, a Jewish prophet and healer who lived in Palestine nearly 2,000 years ago, is central to Christianity. The followers of Jesus established churches whose members sought to continue Jesus' works in particular by preaching the gospel of love and by helping the sick, injured and dying. Many hospitals in the U.K. had their origin in Christian belief and practice. In its institutional forms, Christianity divided first between Catholic and Orthodox, later between Roman Catholic and Protestant and later still into a large number of Christian denominations.

Hospital Chaplains & Visiting Clergy

The NHS Executives have required NHS Trusts to meet the spiritual needs of patients and staff, firstly, by appointing chaplains (full-time or part-time) in consultation with local and national groups represented in the hospital community and, secondly, by facilitating visits by religious leaders or spiritual advisers who visit their members in hospital on a voluntary basis. Christian patients may therefore receive spiritual care from the appropriate chaplain or from the priest, pastor, minister or elder of the local congregation to which the patient belongs. Chaplains are usually available day and night and their services should be called for at the request of a patient or carer or in circumstances of spiritual distress. Their ministry will usually involve:

- Pastoral care and counselling – a listening, supportive, caring relationship often involving the discussion of matters of significance to the patient.
- Acts of Worship – sacraments (Baptism, Holy Communion, Penance – Confession and Absolution, and Anointing), prayers and Bible readings (Bibles are usually available in the ward).

As with all religious ministries, the patient should be given the opportunity to meet with chaplains, or ministers, in quiet, without interruption and if appropriate with the bed screened.

Sunday Services are usually held in a hospital chapel, sanctuary or other place set apart for worship.

Churches in the UK

The main Christian denominations in the UK are

Roman Catholic
Roman Catholic Church

Orthodox
Mostly of Greek, Russian Ukrainian or Serbian extraction, but including
Greek Orthodox Church
Coptic Orthodox Church
Ethiopian Orthodox Church
Syrian Orthodox Church

Protestant (often called Free Churches)
United Reformed Church
Church of Scotland (the established Church in Scotland)
Church of Christ
Presbyterian
Methodist
Baptist
Congregational
Salvation Army
Lutheran
Moravian
Plymouth Brethren
Pentecostal
Black-Majority Churches
Seventh Day Adventist Church
House Churches
Quakers (Religious Society of Friends)
Unitarian and Free Christian Churches

Anglican
The Church of England (the established church in England)
The Scottish Episcopal Church
The Church in Wales
The Church of Ireland

Diet and Fasting

There are no universal dietary regulations. However some Christians will wish to give up certain foods during Lent (a 40-day period, excluding Sundays, between Ash Wednesday and Easter). Equally, some will wish to observe Friday as a no-meat day. Some may wish to fast before receiving Holy Communion. There are also some, particularly those from the protestant churches, who refrain from consuming alcohol. There are no general rules, but again the personal wishes of the patient should be observed.

Family Planning

All churches uphold the sanctity of life and every effort is made to preserve life.

Certain churches discourage their members from using artificial means of contraception

Roman Catholic teaching believes that every life has a divine right to live, including the foetus. Therefore abortion is forbidden.

Birth Customs

There are no specific or universal customs relating to birth itself. However in the event that a baby is stillborn or dies shortly after birth, it is customary for parents to be offered a service of blessing or baptism for their baby. A chaplain or minister usually gives this if available. In their absence, when parents request baptism, members of staff may also perform a baptism by pouring a little water on the baby's forehead and saying; "(Name), I baptise you in the Name of the Father and the Son and the Holy Spirit". Baptists and some other Christians do not practise infant baptism and may prefer that sick or dying babies receive a blessing instead. Staff should follow the wishes of parents.

Blood Transfusions, Ablutions and Toilet Requirements

The golden rule applies; consult the patient whenever possible. (Please read the section on Jehovah's Witnesses)

Death Customs

Dying patients and their carers of all Christian denominations should always be offered the services of the appropriate chaplain. It is important that whenever possible Roman Catholic patients be offered the sacrament known as extreme unction prior to death, or sacrament of anointing the sick.

Some practicing Anglicans may want the administering of sacraments of Communion, anointing, laying on of hands or bedside prayers.

Decisions regarding post-mortems are taken by the next-of-kin according to their individual beliefs and circumstances. As in all cases, bodies of the deceased should always be treated with respect. Most Christians in Britain no longer have formal objection to Cremation.

Worship

Worship may be usual for many Christians and patients should be helped to attend where possible or listen to any relay of a service if available.

CHURCH OF JESUS CHRIST OF LATTER-DAY SAINTS (Mormons)

Estimated Community Size: Global 10,000,000 : UK 170,000

History, Beliefs and Principles

The Church of Jesus Christ of Latter-day Saints arose in America in the early 19th century. The Old and the New Testaments of the Bible are essential scriptures for Latter-day Saints in addition to the Book of Mormon.

The Church of Jesus Christ of Latter-day Saints views the Holy Trinity (Father, Son and Holy Ghost) as three separate and distinct members of a united Godhead. There is a belief in pre-existence: a spirit life prior to birth – but the new infant is born into this world with no memory of that previous life. Life on earth is a period in which to prove oneself worthy to return eventually to live in the presence of Jesus Christ and God the Father. Death is therefore regarded as only temporary separation from the other loved ones.

The Church has no paid ministry, and members serve in a Church 'calling' for a period of time as, perhaps, a teacher or leader. There is, then, no distinction between priests and laymen. The local lay minister is known as a Bishop or a Branch President (depending on the size of the local community). 'Home Teachers', and, for women, 'Visiting Teachers' are given a special assignment to care for Church members and will wish to visit a member in hospital.

Family unity has great importance, epitomised by the 'sealing' ceremony at the Temple, whereby man and wife are sealed together for eternity. Children may be sealed to their parents. Family members, already dead, who were not members of the Church, may be baptised into the faith and sealed to their families, so that they may be together after resurrection.

The Church opposes immorality, pornography, etc, and counsels its members to live moral, honest and upright lives. It teaches sexual purity before marriage and total faithfulness in marriage. It encourages reverence and care for the body, and so counsels against immoral practices and the use of illegal drugs.

Administering to the Sick

As in Biblical time, it is the practice of the Church to *administer* to the sick. Two (generally) members of the local congregations who hold the *priesthood* would – at the request of the person who is ill, or of a relative – visit and perform the administration. One would anoint the sick person with a small amount of consecrated oil, on or near the crown of the head. The second person would then place their hands on the head of the individual and offer a prayer on behalf of the sick person. Some privacy for the administration would be greatly appreciated. Administering to the sick is given to all who request it and is not specifically reserved for the terminally ill or dying. Many members will find comfort in a visit from their Bishop or assigned 'Home Teachers' and the patient or his relatives will know how to contact them. In an emergency, the phone number for the local church building can be found in the phone book.

Family Planning

Husbands must be considerate of their wives, who have the greater responsibility not only for bearing children, but also for caring for them through childhood. Married couples are urged to seek inspiration from the Lord in meeting their marital challenges and rearing their children. They oppose so called "abortion on demand" but recognise there may be rare cases in which an abortion might be considered, e.g. pregnancy as a result of rape or incest, or where the life or health of the woman is in jeopardy.

The Church teaches that sterilisation should only be considered where medical conditions jeopardise life or health, or where birth defects or serious trauma have rendered a person mentally incompetent and not responsible for his or her actions.

Blood Transfusions and Transplants

There is no religious objection to the giving or receiving of blood. The Church encourages blood donation and often makes its meeting houses available for this purpose.

The donation or receiving of organs for transplants is a matter left to individual discretion. Family members are counselled and the decision is one for individuals and families to make, coupled with competent medical advice and confirmation through prayer.

Death Customs

The Church teaches that a living being consists of two elements: the physical body and the spiritual body. Death implies the separation of these two elements. The spiritual body is eternal (it never dies). While the dead physical body is buried or cremated, the spirit waits in paradise for the day of the resurrection.

There is no religious objection to Post Mortem, it would be a matter for the family to decide.

Generally, cremation is not encouraged. The family of the deceased must decide whether to cremate the body taking into account any laws governing burial or cremation.

There are no special rituals associated with dying or death for any age group. Young terminally ill children do not require an emergency baptism. After death, a deceased member should be washed and dressed in a shroud according to hospital protocol.

The Church teaches that a person who participates in euthanasia violates the commandments of God. On the other hand, when dying becomes inevitable, it is looked upon as part of one's eternal existence. Members are taught not to feel obligated to extend mortal life by means that are unreasonable.

Diet

Church members live by a health code known as the *Word of Wisdom*. It warns against the use of stimulants and substances that are harmful to the body, and promotes healthy eating. Because of this, Latter-day Saint patients will abstain from tea, coffee, alcohol and tobacco. However, some will bring in other beverages (e.g. Barley Cup), which simply require the addition of hot water. Hot chocolate, Ovaltine and other such drinks normally available on a hospital ward, are perfectly acceptable. Any prescribed drugs may be taken.

Note

The sacrament of bread and water (Latter-day Saints abstain from alcohol) equates to the Eucharist of other Christians and is performed each Sunday. All members who feel worthy may participate. Although it may be taken in hospital, it would not be regarded as essential for a sick patient.

Special Garments

Those Latter-day Saints who have undergone a special Temple ceremony known as the *endowment* wear sacred undergarments. These intensely private items will normally be worn at all times, day and night. They may be removed by staff in an emergency following an accident, but must at all times be considered sacred and treated with respect. Members will usually refrain from wearing them while in hospital. In the event of death, an 'endowed' member will be buried wearing these and other special clothes, and so members of the Church will come to 'dress' the body prior to burial, by arrangement with the funeral director. Members who have not been to the Temple are not required to wear such clothing.

National Contact

751 Warwick Road
Solihull
B91 3DQ
Tel: 0121 711 2244

JEHOVAH'S WITNESSES
130 – 250,000 (Witnesses and sympathisers)

History, Beliefs and Principles

Jehovah's Witnesses are a Christian religion whose members accept the Bible as the word of God and endeavour to live by the laws and principles contained therein.

Founded by Charles Taze Russell in the late 1800s

The principal consideration for Jehovah's Witnesses who have been hospitalised relates to their sincerely held and Bible-based view that taking blood into one's body is morally wrong. They believe that medical treatment is a matter for the informed consent of the individual and although Jehovah's Witnesses will not accept treatment involving the use of blood or blood components, they are pleased to co-operate with medical and nursing staff in other forms of management.

In an effort to be helpful they have established an international network of Hospital Liaison Committees, which includes 36 in Britain, who are able to assist in locating sympathetic consultants for the alternative non-blood medical management of their members. The Hospital Information Desk at their headquarters (see address below) will be pleased to put you in contact with the Hospital Liaison Committee Chairman in your locality.

Worship

Local units of the Jehovah's Witness organisation are called congregations, and worship takes place in Kingdom Halls.

Diet

Other than the rejection of foods containing blood, they are no special dietary needs. Some Jehovah's Witnesses may be vegetarian or teetotal, but this is a personal decision. Jehovah's Witnesses do not smoke or use other tobacco products.

Death Customs

Jehovah's Witnesses have no special rituals or practices for the dying, but a patient who is terminally ill will no doubt appreciate a pastoral visit from one of their elders and are always grateful if these are accorded the privileges customarily given by hospitals to ministers of religion. The dead may be either buried or cremated, depending on personal or family preferences and local circumstances. There are no specified funeral rites, though a simple, personal service will likely be held at the deceased's Kingdom Hall (church) or at the crematorium or graveside.

They have no over-riding religious objections to post-mortem examinations, but unless there is a compelling reason Jehovah's Witnesses generally prefer that the body of a beloved relative is not subject to dissection. The appropriate relatives will make a personal decision regarding autopsy to determine cause of death. In their view, the use of cadaveric material for research or transplantation is also a matter for personal, conscientious decision.

Family Planning

Deliberately induced abortion simply to avoid the birth of an unwanted child is the wilful taking of human life and hence is unacceptable to Jehovah's Witnesses. If at the time of childbirth a choice must be made between the life of the mother and that of the child, it is up to the individuals concerned to make that decision.

Every effort is made to assist the natural parent(s) to care for their children and to preserve, to the extent possible, the integrity of the family. If custodian care by others is necessary, the best physical, emotional, and spiritual environment is desirable and encouraged.

Blood Transfusions and Transplants

Jehovah's Witnesses carry on their person an Advance Medical Directive/Release that directs no blood transfusions be given under any circumstances, while releasing medical practitioners/hospitals of the responsibility for any damage that might be caused by their refusal of blood. When entering the hospital, consent/release forms should be signed that state matters similarly and deal more specifically with the hospital care needed.

Note: Immunoglobulins, Vaccines, Organs

The religious understanding of Jehovah's Witnesses does not absolutely prohibit the use of minor blood fractions such as albumin, immune globulins and haemophiliac preparations. Each Witness must decide individually whether he can accept these. Accepting vaccines from a non-blood source is a medical decision to be made by each one. While the Bible specifically forbids consuming blood, no Biblical command pointedly forbids the taking in of tissue or bone from another human. Therefore, whether to accept an organ transplant or donate organs is a personal, medical decision.

Decision-Making and Treatment Information

The patient (or parents/guardians of young children) should be fully informed on diagnosis, prognosis and treatment recommendations so that informed health care decisions can be made. Parents have the natural and legal right to make such decisions for their children. In a rare emergent situation where doctors may feel the need to get a court order to impose medical care to which the parents have not given consent (such as administering a blood transfusion), the parents should be informed of such intended action as early as possible so that they can be represented in court also.

Prolongation of Life and Right to Die

Life is sacred and the wilful taking of life under any health care circumstances would be wrong. For this reason, reasonable and humane effort should be made to sustain and prolong life. However, the Scriptures do not require that extraordinary, complicated, distressing, and costly measures be taken to sustain a person, if such, in the general consensus of the attending medical practitioners, would merely prolong the dying process and/or leave the patient with no quality of life. Any advance directions by the patient that specifically defined what was or was not wanted should be respected.

National Contact

Watchtower House
The Ridgeway
London NW7 1RP
Telephone 0208-906-2211

HINDUS
'Who sees all beings in his own Self, and his own Self in all beings, loses all fear.' ('The Upanishads')
Estimated Community Size: Global 811,000,000 : UK 400,000 – 550,000

History, Beliefs and Principles

The Indian community in Britain is comprised mostly of Indians from Gujarat State who came directly from India or East Africa in the 1950's and 60s. Hinduism is the majority religion in India.

For Hindus, the purpose of human life is to make a conscious effort to communicate with God. By living a moral and ethical life, serving his fellow men and creatures, man can make spiritual contact with God the Creator and Supreme Spirit, and therefore realise God. The spirit is worshipped through 3 images; Brahma, Vishnu and Shiva. Hindus also believe that if they are not able to realise God in this life, they will be born again (through reincarnation) in this world to continue their pilgrimage until Moksha (salvation). A Hindu's destiny in life is known as Dharma, and their situation in life is determined by actions in previous lives – this is known as Karma.

Care and concern for all beings is fundamental to Hinduism, and is often shown through individual acts of kindness. For example, every pious Hindu is expected to keep aside some food for the arrival of an unexpected guest – no one should be turned away hungry from his door. 'Guests invited or not should be treated like the Lord Himself.' Because of the sacredness of all life, 'ahinsa' (non-injury) is cherished as one of the highest principles. This makes Hindus reluctant to consume other creatures as food.

Predominant Languages

The main language is Gujarati, but the national language of India is Hindi. In Britain many younger Indians are likely to speak and write English fluently, although it may still be a second language for some. Older generations may speak little or no English.

It should be noted that there are over 100 languages and dialects in India. However the most common languages are:-

Bengali, Punjabi, Hindi, Gujarati, Tamil, Telugu, Sanskrit (for worship)

Religious Texts

There is no single holy book. The four main religious holy books are The Bhagavatgita, the Upanishads, The Ramayana and the Mahabharata.

Religious Festivals

There are many Hindu festivals. The main ones are

Diwali or Deepawali (Festival of lights)
Holi (Spring festival)
Navaratri (Festival of nine nights)

Worship

Worship (Pujah) can take place in a temple (Mandir) or at home, where a temple or shrine exists. Hindus will usually wish to pray twice daily. Where possible incense will be burnt, and holy books and prayer beads are required. Hindus worship God through different symbolic deities and images, used to personify divine qualities. The 'gods and goddesses' are used as symbols of the Divine. Depending on what a person wants to achieve, they worship that particular form as a *facet* of the One Reality – God. God is symbolised by the word Om or Aum.

Dress

Dress codes are observed mainly by older women. They tend to wear a Sari or Punjabi suit (2 piece dress worn over trousers). Men tend to wear western clothes. Women may also wear bangles or a thread – these should not be rmoved without permission. Some Hindus wear a read spot on their foreheads or scalp. Again these should not be removed or washed off without permission.

Names

A Hindu patient is likely to have *three* names – personal name first, a complimentary name in the middle, then a family name: e.g. Arima Kumari Chopra. For Gujerati men the middle name is the father's personal name plus an ending: e.g. Mohandas Karamchand Gandhi. Women do not usually use their father's personal name as a middle name, so they have only personal and family names. Using the family 'surname' for records.

Diet

Hindus are in the main vegetarians. The cow is a sacred animal and therefore even meat eating Hindus may not eat beef. Some will eat eggs, some not: it is best to ask each individual. Dairy produce is acceptable, so long as it is free of animal fat; some Hindus will eat only cottage cheese – again, the best thing to do is check with the individual. It is important to remember that strict vegetarians will be unhappy about eating even vegetarian items if they are served from the same plate or with the same utensils as meat due to potential cross contamination. Apart from practices based on religious beliefs, some Indians may have strongly held traditional ideas about taking certain foods at particular times – for example, it is considered unwise to take milk or any citrus fruit when suffering from a cough.

Fasting

Although fasting is a regular feature of the Hindu religion, very few Hindus would insist on fasting when in hospital due it being a physically demanding exercise. Fasting may require abstinence from only certain foods. At the end of each period of fasting, visitors may bring in 'prasad' so that the patient can join in the celebration. This will be in the form of a small quantity of food, perhaps sweets, which have been offered to God in thanksgiving and is now shared amongst those present.

Birth Customs

Relatives will be anxious that the mother has complete rest for 40 days after birth – they will be very worried if she has to get up for a bath within the first few days, for example. This attitude is based on the belief that a women is at her weakest at this time and very susceptible to chills, backaches etc. On the other hand it may require considerable tact and persuasion to reconcile the mother to her baby being placed in a separate room, if the hospital's procedures require this. Visiting relatives will sometimes have to be persuaded to leave gifts of clothing for the baby at the bedside, rather than putting them on straight away.

Death Customs

If a Hindu patient is dying in hospital relatives may wish to bring money and clothes for him to touch before distribution to the needy.

They will wish to keep a bedside vigil - if the visitors are not allowed to go to the bedside themselves, they will be grateful if a nurse can do this for them while they wait. Some relatives will welcome an opportunity to sit with the dying patient and read from a holy book. After death the body should always be left covered. Relatives will wish to wash the body and put on new clothes before taking it from the hospital. Traditionally the eldest son of the deceased should take a leading part in this, however young he may be – including dispatching the coffin to the flames at the crematorium. If a post-mortem is unavoidable, Hindus will be anxious that all organs are returned to the body before cremation (or burial for children under five years old) – to safeguard peace in the afterlife. If someone wants to donate his or her organ it is permissible.

Attitudes to Medical and Social Work Staff and Illness

Generally speaking, Hindu patients will willingly accept the authority of the professional, whether male or female. They are inclined to favour home remedies for ailments such as coughs, and be slow to seek professional attention.

Blood Transfusions and Transplants

These present no problems for Hindus.

Family Planning

There is no objection to family planning from the religious point of view. However, there may be strong social pressures on the women – particularly if no son has yet been born – and it is advisable to involve her husband in any discussion of family planning.

Washing and Toilet

Hindus will need water for washing in the same room as the W.C. itself. If there is no tap there, or if a bed-pan has to be used, they will be grateful to have a container of water provided. Hindu patients much prefer to wash in free flowing water, rather than sitting in a bath. As Indian food is eaten using the fingers, the washing of hands before and after meals is customary. It is regarded as unclean to use the same hand that is used for toileting as that for eating or performing religious ceremonies.

Ideas of Modesty

As with all Asian patients, a Hindu woman is likely to have strong preference for a female doctor when being examined or treated. They should be accommodated in mixed wards only in emergency situations. An open-minded and helpful approach can save the patient embarrassment – for example a female patient finds it difficult to accept an X-ray gown because of its shortness.

National Contact

In the UK there is no single representative organisation of Hindus. However the Hindu Council of the UK was set up as an umbrella organisation in 1994.

Hindu Council (UK)
74 Llanover Road
North Wembley
HA9 7LT

JAINS

'Malice to none but love and fraternity to all.' (Jain greeting)
Estimated Community Size: Global 4,200,000 : UK 25,000 – 30,000

History, Beliefs and Principles

Arguably, Jainism is one of the oldest religions of the world.
Jainism believes that a living being consists of gross physical body,
subtle luminous and karmic body and the soul. We can experience
physical body with our sense, but the subtle bodies and the soul are
not sense perceptible. They can be perceived by the direct
knowledge from the inner self and require long practice of
spirituality and mediation.

Jains do not believe in a supreme creator god; the universe has
always existed. Instead, they revere 24 luminary teachers
(conquerors or pathfinders or tirthankaras) of their faith and
worship them as exemplary heroes for guiding them to the perfect
path of liberation. Majavira, the last and most recent teacher (6th
century BCE), who revived and reformulated Jainism, is especially
honoured. He taught in the colloquial language rather than in
Sanskrit.

Jainism believes in the equality of all souls, irrespective of caste,
creed or colour and reverence for life in its totality. It accords
significance to the minutest living organisms. Animal welfare,
vegetarianism and care of the environment are very much at the
heart of Jain beliefs. The belief in relative pluralism or multiplicity
of views has made Jains tolerant towards other faiths. They are
encouraged to follow certain key principles:

> *Non-violence*, not harming any living creature even the
> smallest life forms, either physically or mentally. As an
> extension of non-violence, Jains are encouraged to show
> friendship and love towards everyone, to hold malice
> towards none, and to practice forgiveness and self-
> discipline.
>
> *Truthfulness*, including not harming another through
> one's speech. Honesty and not stealing.

Non-materialism, not attaching importance to material things. Chastity and sexual continence, not being sexually promiscuous.

Multiplicity of views or perspectives, the belief that no one perspective on any issue is the whole truth. Thus Jainism encourages tolerance and acceptance of other's believes.

Although Jainism and Hinduism have different origins and histories, since the two religions have lived side by side in India for thousands of years, they share some common traditions and practices.

Predominant Languages

Bengali, Punjabi, Hindi, Gujarati, Tamil, Telugu, Sanskrit (for worship)

Names

A Jain patient is likely to have three names: a personal first name, a complimentary middle name, and a family surname, which should be used for their medical records. In general, it is polite to use a title plus the surname when addressing the patient – especially if they are elderly.

Worship

Most Jains worship three times a day: in the morning, around noon and before sunset, but the most important is the Morning Prayer. Jains may chant their mantras in silence, but occasionally out loud, and may use a strong of beads – like a rosary – but most appreciate privacy and not being disturbed when they are praying. Some Jains may listen to recording of prayers and sermons.

Diet

The overwhelming majority of Jains in the UK follow a strictly vegetarian diet. Although Jains drink milk, some may not eat butter or cheese because of the minute organisms they contain. For the same reason, most Jains abstain from alcohol as well as root vegetables, including onions, garlic, potatoes, carrots, and figs and honey. Due to emphasis on non-violence towards any living thing, the majority of Jains do not eat meat, fish or eggs or any food made from or containing them. Jains, who eat any of these, even unknowingly are likely to feel revulsion and also spiritually polluted. When preparing or serving meals it is extremely important to keep meat, fish, eggs and other prohibited food strictly segregated from food intended for Jain patients. Some older, more conservative, Jains may also be distressed if meat, eggs or fish are served to others in their presence. They may prefer to eat alone with the curtains drawn or in another area.

Some Jains only eat during daylight hours. This tradition arose as in the days before electricity it was often difficult to see what one was eating after dark, and there was a risk that some living organisms may be harmed. Check with Jain patients whether they follow this practice and discuss how best they can be accommodated.

If an Asian vegetarian diet is available in hospital, ask the Jain patients if this is acceptable to them or if they need special food; if so, most families are willing to bring in food providing facilities are available for storage and heating.

Fasting

Fasting is an important area of a Jain's spiritual life. Some Jains fast regularly on the 5th and/or 14th day of each lunar month, women are especially likely to fast. During the fast, Jains will not take anything except boiled water during the day, and some may not even take that. Neither will they take solids, except in semi-fasting when they may take one or two meals a day. They may also fast for a week during the festival of Paryusana-parva in August or September. However, it is unlikely that Jain will fast if they are very ill.

Birth Customs

It is customary for the mother to take complete rest for 40 days, but she will adjust to the health needs and the rules of the hospital. Relatives help the mother to cope with the strain of the delivery and the care of the baby.

Death Customs

A Jain who is seriously ill or dying may receive comfort from mediation, the worship of holy images, prayer beads, prayer books, and recordings of mantras and prayers. Jains believe the individual should have good thoughts with the feeling of detachment at the deathbed and hence a patient may wish to die in auspicious mediation or listening to auspicious mantras and prayers. For the patient's family, it is extremely important that everyone should be there, and this may require accommodating a large number of people. Relatives may wish to chant or pray with the patient. Even if the patient appears unconscious, a relative may wish to chant in the patient's ear as the latter may be able to hear at some level, and some may wish to burn incense.

Repentance, confession and penance are very important Jain beliefs, and the patient may wish to ask for forgiveness from relatives and friends if they have harmed them knowingly or unknowingly. The patient may wish to make a donation to a charitable cause. In rare cases, when a patient is elderly, very ill or for whom no further treatment is appropriate, may decide very gradually to withdraw from the world. This decision to undertake a 'holy death' is not taken lightly and should be respected. They may fast for long periods of time, reducing their food intake until only fluids are taken, and then finally reducing even their fluid intake. They may also refuse all medication.

Attitudes towards Medical Staff and Illness

Some Jains may choose to avoid certain drugs: Due to the prohibition against harming any form of life, some Jains may prefer not to take any antibiotics. However, if antibiotics are essential, most Jains will accept them but may do so with regret. Some Jains may also be reluctant to take opiates, due to their emphasis on endurance, self-discipline and suffering. They may prefer to rely on spiritual practices or human support and comfort rather than medical means of alleviating pain, but they will co-operate with the medical staff and obey their instructions.

Blood Transfusions and Transplants

These are not a problem and in principle there is no objection to organ donation.

Family Planning

This is not a problem for Jains, but they will avoid abortion if contraception fails. Hence prescribe the safest contraceptive method and give a full explanation.

Washing and Toilet

This is not a problem for Jains, but some patients may prefer water for washing.

Ideas of Modesty

As with all Asian patients, Jain women are likely to require a female doctor when being treated or examined, and will accept only a single sex ward.

National Contact

Institute of Jainology
Unit 18, Silicon Business Centre
26-28 Wandsworth Road
Greenford UB6 7JZ
Tel: 020 89972300

JEWS

'Hear, O Israel, the Lord our God, the Lord is one, and you shall love the Lord your God with all your heart and with all your soul and with all your might.' (The 'Shema')

Estimated Community Size: Global 14,500,000 : UK 283,000

History, Beliefs and Principles

Judaism has been in existence for five-and-a-half thousand years and was founded by the prophet Abraham. It is based on the belief in one universal God seen by Jews in a purely personal relationship. The love of God and the wish to carry out the Ten Commandments as given to Moses on Mount Sinai is embodied in the teaching of the Pentateuch, the first five books of the Old Testament, a portion of which is read every Sabbath in synagogues throughout the country. The religious precepts followed are simply to worship one God, to carry out the Ten Commandments, to practice charity and tolerance towards one's fellow human beings.

Jewish religion and culture are inextricably mixed. There are a number of different Jewish traditions present in the UK, each with different levels and styles of observance, from the most observant (Orthodox, Hasidic, Haredim) to Conservative (Masorti) to Progressive (Reform and Liberal). It should be noted that after many centuries of dispersal from their land of origin, Israel, many Jews have adopted food habits, habits of dress and modes of behaviour of the host countries and generally those Jews likely to be hospitalised in Britain will be totally European.

Worship

Observing Jewish men and women pray 3 times per day in the morning, afternoon and evening. Prayer shawls and a leather box containing biblical texts (Phylacteries) will be worn during some sessions. The Jewish Sabbath (Shabbat) begins before nightfall on Friday afternoon and ends with the first sighting of three stars on Saturday night. Orthodox Jews will not write, travel or work, switch on electrical appliances or cook on the Sabbath. It is a 'day of rest' and there are synagogue services on Friday evenings and Saturday mornings. Additionally orthodox congregations attend discussion groups on the holy books together with their Rabbis on Saturday afternoons. As the Sabbath ends, a candle is lit and a blessing given for the coming week. Note – in emergencies any necessary activity is permitted on Shabbat if life or health is threatened.

Predominant Languages

English – Used by Jews in the UK as the everyday language of communication

Hebrew – the language of the Bible, of prayer and in Israel Hebrew is wide spoken and written. However here in Britain Hebrew is the principally the language of worship, rather than of everyday communication

Yiddish – a Jewish language of Eastern European origin used conversationally by some.

Religious Texts

Judaism is derived from Jewish scriptures as interpreted by Rabbis(teachers). These are known as Tenakh – an acronym of the names of the 3 sections Torah (teaching), Nevi'im (books of prophets) and Keturim (writings)

Names

Jewish names are not structured differently to the British system

Religious Festivals

No strict dates can be given in the Gregorian calendar as the Jewish calendar is lunar. The main festivals are

Rosh Hashana – New Year - Sep / Oct
Yom Kippur – Day of Atonement – Sep/ Oct (10 days after Rosh Hashana)
Sukkot – Tabernacles – Oct
Pesach – Passover – 8 day festival in Mar / Apr

Dress

Observant Jews are required to dress modestly. Many orthodox men wear a skullcap (yarmulke). Some men wear their hair in side locks – these must not be cut unless there is a clear medical need. Many orthodox women cover their heads with a headscarf or wig – again medical staff should keep the head covered at all times unless removal is required for medical reasons.

Diet

Jews eat only meat which is killed by their own religious-trained personnel in a humanitarian way; this ensures that as much blood as possible is drained from the meat before it is prepared by soaking and salting, then cooked. It would be extremely unusual for a Jewish patient to eat pork in any form; the pig and horse are totally forbidden animals. Jews who are observant will not take meat and milk at the same meal, and prefer at least a three-hour wait between these kinds of foods. A kosher household will keep meat and milk utensils, crockery and cutlery rigidly separate. The very orthodox are prepared to avoid any suspect food, and an item such as cheddar cheese may be refused because it contains animal rennet from a non-kosher animal; and the same applies to jellies containing gelatine. Jews will eat eggs and white fish; but there are prohibitions on shellfish and fish lacking fins and scales. The teachings of the religion do stress that to avoid a deterioration in health, some laxity may be allowed: a Jew who would not eat out in a restaurant because of the risk of inadvertently eating from plates which have contained forbidden foods or which have been part of a mixed washing-up, will take a cup of tea or a plate of cereal in order to avoid undue health risk. The meat of wild birds is also prohibited.

Observant Jews may request a vegetarian hospital diet, as this avoids the need to make special requests in order to avoid eating non-kosher meat. However, deep frozen kosher meals are usually available through the Hospital Kosher Meals Service: In larger towns and cities the local Jewish community can arrange for kosher food throughout the patient's stay in hospital – the patient ensuring that any fee or donation for this service is paid.

Fasting

There are several minor fasts in the religious calendar but the prominent fast which almost every Jew observes is Yom-Kippur, the day of atonement, a 25-hour fast, usually falling in late September/October. If health permits a Jew would prefer to keep that day and also to pray and to be quiet and penitential. It is the holiest day of the Jewish calendar, one that is considered to set the path for the year to follow.

Birth Customs

Judaism is a family orientated religion, therefore the birth of a child is a very joyful and shared occasion. If the child is a boy, circumcision will take place on the eighth day after birth, providing the child is well; the circumcision is always delayed if there is the slightest doubt about the child's health. The ritual is performed by a trained and medically certificated religious functionary, often the local minister. If the mother and child are still at the hospital, a small room may be requested and the men of the family will attend the ritual and name the child. Today it is usual for the mother and child to have returned home by the eighth day so that a hospital may not be called upon to participate in any way.

Death Customs

Death has its rites. No mutilation of the body is allowed unless there is a legal requirement for a post-mortem. The funeral usually takes place within 24 hours and cremation is forbidden. Depending on the sex of the deceased, a fellow male or female prepares the body for burial; usually three members of the community are present. The body is washed and shrouded before being placed in the coffin. Prayers are said. There is a family mourning period of seven days, during which prayers are said and mourners visit the bereaved household.

Attitudes to Medical and Social Work Staff and Illness

The medical professional is treated with great respect. There is very little mystique about medicine within the community and medical staffs are likely to find that the patient and his family ask many pertinent questions. Probably the close-knit family ties will bring some extra questioning from the relatives. Since there is a requirement upon the Jews to be aware of bodily function of diet, ablution and mode of life, they are likely to be an aware and questioning patient.

Transfusions and Transplants

It is essential to deal with each situation individually as changing medico-ethical views and practices in Israel and elsewhere may well influence attitudes amongst Orthodox Jews. This said, most Jews will have no objections to transfusions and transplants.

Family Planning

While mechanical methods of contraception are not strictly permitted, today almost all Jews will use some method of family limitation. The pill is widely used.

Washing and Toilet

Jews are religiously enjoined to wash their hands and say a brief blessing before eating. Some orthodox Jews do not bathe or shower during major festivals or Shabbat and some men prefer to be bearded or will only use an electric razor (a modern circumvention of a ruling against shaving).

Ideas of Modesty

Many modern Jewish women are prepared to be examined and treated by male doctors, and attitudes are probably indistinguishable from those of the majority female population. However in Orthodox Judaism touch between woman and man is forbidden unless married and there is therefore a preference for same-sex care.

National Contact

Board of Deputies of British Jews
Commonwealth House
1-19 New Oxford Street
London WC1A 1NU
020 7543 5400

MUSLIMS

Praise be to Allah, the Lord of the worlds! The compassionate, the merciful! Guide us on the straight path.' (Sura 1 of the 'Qur'an')

Estimated Community Size: Global 1,188,000,000 : UK 1,000,000 – 1,500,000

History, Beliefs and Principles

Islam is the fastest growing religion in the world. In Britain the majority of Muslims are permanently settled from India and Pakistan or visitors and students from South East Asia, Africa and the Middle East Arabic countries, but there are Muslims to be found from all over the world.

Although the fundamental beliefs and principles of Islam are universal, different Islamic traditions exist. The two principal branches are Sunni (90% of all Muslims) and Shia (10%) and within these branches there exist different denominations with their own interpretations, practices and ways of expressing their faith.

Within the Sunni tradition the principal schools of thought are Barelwi, Deobandi, Tablighi Jamaat, Ahl-e-Hadith and Jamaat-I-Islami.

Within the Shia tradition there are the Twelvers (Ithna Asherites) and Seveners (Ismaelis).

Sufism is a mystical strand of Islam that can be found in both the Sunni and Shia traditions.

Finally, there is the Ahmadiyya Community, who profess to believe in the fundamental teachings of Islam and yet are often rejected by other followers of Islam.

These varying practices and beliefs mean that is important not to assume that someone who says they are Muslim will adhere to everything set out in this chapter. Always ask the individual.

Islam is an Arabic word and connotes submission to the will of God. The other literal meaning of Islam is 'Peace'. Islam is established on two principal bases of faith:

1. There is no other God worth worshipping except Allah

2. Mohammed (peace be upon him) is the last prophet sent by God for mankind.

Whoever honestly believes in and professes the Unity of God and the prophethood of Mohammed (peace be upon him) joins the fold of Islam and is a Muslim. Islam is based on five fundamental principles that should be completely practised by every Muslim.

1. Shahadah: The declaration of faith that there is no one worthy of worship but Allah and that Mohammed is the messenger
2. Salat: To establish daily five stated prayers.
3. Ramadan: fasting in the month of Ramadan requires abstaining from food and drink and sexual contact from dawn to sunset.
4. Zakat: Regular charity – charity to the poor is obligatory and binding.
5. Hajj: - Pilgrimage to Mecca – it is an incumbent duty to be performed once a lifetime if one can afford it.

Muslims affirm the Torah brought by Moses and the Gospel of Jesus and believe that the Prophet Mohammed (PBUH) was the last in a succession of messengers, completing the earlier teachings of Abraham, Moses and Jesus through revelations that came to him via the Angel Jibreel (Gabriel).

Predominant Languages

Many languages may be found amongst Muslims due to the diverse nature of the UK Muslim population. Some of the most likely to be found are:

Arabic, Bengali, Farsi, Gujarati, Hausa, Malay, Punjabi, Pushto, Sylheti (spoken only), Turkish, Urdu

Religious Texts

The Muslim Holy Book is the Qur'an – it is the revelation of Allah as revealed to the Prophet Muhammed (PBUH).
The language of the Qur'an is Arabic.

Religious Festivals

The Muslim calendar is lunar, meaning that festival dates cannot be conclusively dated far in advance as they depend on the sighting of the new moon for the beginning of a new month.

Eid al-Fitr: This festival marks the end of the Ramadan month of fasting

Eid al-Adha: The festival of sacrifice that marks the end of Hajj

Milad al-Nabi: Celebration of the birthday of the holy prophet

Dress

Muslim women are required to cover their whole body other than for the face and hands. Clothing must be loose enough not to show shape or outline of the body. More orthodox women will also cover face with a veil as well as covering hands. Muslim men are also required to dress conservatively.

Worship

Muslims will pray 5 times daily - the First early in the morning before sunrise, second at noon, third midway between noon and sunset, fourth at sunset, fifth at night – these can be performed in a Mosque or at home. The sacred day is Friday. They pray facing the direction of Qibla (facing Mecca).

Muslims will want to maintain their normal prayer while ill wherever possible. If they are mobile they should be offered privacy – ideally a clean, separate room set aside for the purpose. If this is not possible as, for example a hospital patient is bed bound, then curtains should be drawn. Before prayer Muslims should wash hands, face and feet in running water (see Washing and Toilet section below)

Names

As with other Asian patients, confusion may arise when recording names. A Muslim may have several personal or religious names and sometimes also a family name – for example, Amjad Mohammed Hussein. If there is a family name use it for the records, if not, establish the main personal name and use it.

Diet

Lamb, beef, goat, chicken and rabbit etc are allowed provided these are killed by a Muslim with a religious prayer (Halal food). Pakistanis are particularly strict about eating only Halal meat. Pork meat, all products from pork, carrion and blood are forbidden, as are all types of alcohol. In Britain Muslims buy their meat from a Muslim butcher, which is available according to Islamic injunctions. A Muslim does not eat meat or food generally available in the shops which contain animal fats, fearing it may contain pork fat or fat from animals not ritually slaughtered. Fish and eggs are allowed, although again strict separation in preparation is essential. It is certainly not acceptable simply to remove a slice of pork from a plate and then offer the plate to the patient again. Unless absolutely sure that all food is Halal, when away from home many Muslims will follow a vegetarian diet.

Both Pakistanis and Arabs like their food well seasoned and spiced and bland food may be considered unpalatable.

Fasting

During the month of Ramadan a Muslim eats before observing his fast, that is 1½ hours before sunrise, and is allowed to eat and drink all lawful things after sunset. The sick or infirm are not obliged to fast. Fasting is also excused during menstruation and after a recent childbirth. Equally, those on a journey or breastfeeding their babies are not asked to fast, but they should make up for this later. However some may wish to fast (abstaining from all food, water and medication during daylight hours), and every effort should be made to facilitate fasting – this would include providing patients with adequate and acceptable meals during the hours of darkness and wherever possible, medication should be adjusted to fit in with the fast. If the doctor feels it is important that the patient should eat and drink more, it is useful to explain that this is in fact part of the medicine to assist recovery. It is important to recognise any decision to fast as one based on different priorities and not one of ignorance or non adherence.

Birth Customs

Some women may refuse to be examined internally before giving birth. When a Muslim child is born it is required that as soon as possible a member of the family recites in the baby's ear a prayer which normally lasts a minute or two (Azaan). A male Muslim is also required to be circumcised as soon as possible.

Death Customs

The dying Muslim will wish to lie on their right side facing Qibla. Comfort can be provided by familiar people reading to the patient verses from the Qur'an and by the patient themselves reciting the declaration of faith (Kalima). It is an important religious duty to visit the sick and dying so there may be large numbers of visitors at all hours.

It is customary amongst Pakistanis and Arabs to express their emotion freely when a relative dies. Whenever possible they should be given privacy to do so; and the need to avoid disturbing other patients by their mourning should be gently but firmly explained.

The next-of-kin will want to arrange for the washing of the body before burial. In Islam it is required to bury a body as quickly as possible (cremation is forbidden). It is necessary to avoid post-mortem if legally possible, as this is not allowed and causes considerable distress; organs should all be buried with the body.

Attitudes to Medical and Social Work Staff and Illness

A Muslim believes that whatever takes place, good or bad, can only take place with the consent of Allah and according to his judgement and distinction, as nothing can happen in this domination against his Will. In adversity and calamity a Muslim is forbidden to despair and is required to be patient, seeking help through prayers and remembrance of Allah.

Blood Transfusions and Transplants

The question of organ donation has been much discussed and, although it has been declared as permitted, it is a complicated issue and will often be met with reluctance. As always, the decision lies with the individuals and their family, who if they wish can consult their local religious leaders.

Family Planning

Strictly speaking an orthodox Muslim would not approve of family planning devices. In practice individuals will vary widely in their attitudes: information about facilities available should be given, but no pressure exerted. Any discussion should be in strict confidence, and never in front of visiting relatives or friends.

Washing and Toilet

Muslims attach great importance to cleanliness. They need water in toilets (toilet paper is not considered adequate); if a bedpan has to be used a container of clean water should accompany it. Muslims prefer to wash in free flowing water, and cannot accept the idea of sitting in a bath. Ablution before each prayer is necessary. The worshipper washes hands, rinses mouth, cleans nostrils, washes face, arms up to the elbows, wets hands and runs them through the hair (to remove any dust or particles), cleans inside and behind the ears and lastly washes his feet up to the ankles – each of the above three times. After menstruation women are required to wash their whole bodies. It is regarded as unclean to use the same hand that is used for toileting as that for eating or performing religious ceremonies.

Ideas of Modesty

Generally a Muslim woman is not allowed to be examined or be surrounded by male members of medical staff. It is always preferable that a female member of the medical staff is present. In certain cases a Muslim woman may not agree at all to be examined or treated by a male member of the medical staff. In Islam free mixing of sexes is prohibited. Islamic law (Sharia) states that there should be no physical contact between a woman and any man other than her husband. Muslims should be accommodated in mixed wards only in emergency situations. This is an area in which an open-minded and helpful approach by staff could be particularly helpful – for example when a female patient finds it difficult to accept an X-ray gown because of its shortness.

National Contact

Muslim Council of Britain
PO Box 52
Wembley
HA9 0XW
Tel: 020 89039024

PAGANS

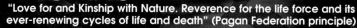

"Love for and Kinship with Nature. Reverence for the life force and its ever-renewing cycles of life and death" (Pagan Federation principle)

History, Beliefs and Principles

Paganism is not a classical, structured religion – but rather an outlook that has its roots in the indigenous nature-religions of Europe, evolved and adapted to the circumstances of modern life. Pagans seek to lead ethical lives in harmony with Nature, and see Deity as manifest within the natural world.

Within Paganism there are a number of distinct traditions including the Craft (Witchcraft or Wicca), Druidry, Shamanism and Odinism. These different disciplines are united in the common Pagan root belief of the spirituality of the natural world.

Worship

Most Pagans worship the old, pre-Christian, Gods and Goddesses of this land through seasonal festivals and other ceremonies. Observance of these festivals is very important to Pagans, and those in hospital will generally wish to celebrate them in some form.

Religious Festivals

The main seasonal festivals are Samhain (31st October), Yule (21st December) Imbolc (1st Feb), Spring Equinox (21st Mar), Beltane (30th Apr), Midsummer (21st Jun), Lughnasadh (1st August) and Autumn Equinox (21 Sept).

Diet

Many Pagans are vegetarians, some are also vegans. Many of those who eat meat will object to that derived from intensively farmed stock – a practice which Pagans regard as immoral and cruel.

Birth Customs

As Paganism celebrates life, birth is viewed as both sacred and empowering. Pagan women will wish to make their own, informed, decisions regarding prenatal and neonatal care.

Death Customs

Pagans accept death as a natural part of life. Pagans will wish to know when they are dying so that they may consciously prepare for it. Most Pagans believe in some form of reincarnation. Some families will wish to take the body home to prepare it for burial or cremation themselves, others will employ funeral directors.

Attitudes to Medical Staff and Illness

Pagans tend to use complementary therapies as a matter of course, and may wish to continue doing so in hospital. They also embrace conventional medicine and will hold its practitioners in respect. Pagans are likely to be well-informed and questioning patients.

Family Planning

Pagans will generally plan pregnancies, and use contraception as appropriate. Paganism emphasises women's control over their own bodies, and the weighty decisions relating to abortion are seen as a personal matter for the women concerned, who will be supported in the choices she makes.

Ideas of Modesty

Pagans are not ashamed of their bodies, and will generally be relaxed about medical examinations.

National Contact

Pagan Federation
BM Box 7079
London
WC1N 3XX

RASTAFARIANS

'O thou God of Ethiopia, thou God of divine majesty, thy spirit come within our hearts to dwell in the parts of righteousness. That the hungry be fed, the sick nourished, the aged protected and the infant cared for.'
(Rastafarian prayer)

History, Beliefs and Principles

A religious and political movement centred in the Caribbean and inspired by Marcus Garvey in the 1920s and 1930s. It is a cult of Ras Tafari, better known as Haile Selassie (ce 1892 – 1975), Emperor of Ethiopia (1930-74), who is regarded as the Messiah of the Black Race. The 'Lion of Judah' symbol represents Haile Selassie. Rastafarians believe that all West Indians came from Ethiopia and will return there to liberation. In many ways it is a way of life rather than a religion although it has many links with Christianity and Judaism. The beliefs are based on the Bible, especially the Old Testament, and the Book of Revelation in the New Testament. Rastafarians helped develop the *reggae* style of soul music, which they use to express their political and religious aspirations. The singer Bob Marley has became one of the heroes of the movement.

Principal Languages

English Rastafarians main language is English, Creole or Patois. Forms may vary, however some examples of distinctive words and phrases used, are "Irie", a form of greeting and recognition. Rastafarians refer to men as "bretherens" and women as "sisterens". "I and I", which may mean "I singular as well as "I" plural. "Man" and "woman" are both singular and plural. "Jah" means "God"

Names

English or Africanised names are used.

Worship

Cannabis may be used in worship

Dress

Hair is worn as dreadlocks, which symbolise the Rastafarian roots and, because of the way the hair grows, the 'Lion of Judah'. They usually keep their heads covered, women with a wrap or a tam, and men with a tam (tams are knitted, leather or cloth). They also wear items in the red, gold and green colours of the Ethiopian flag.

Diet

Rastafarians do not eat any pork or fish with scales. Most do not eat any meat. Fresh, natural and organic foods are preferred to processed foods. Most Rastafarians use marijuana and view it as a religious rite.

Birth Customs

Natural methods are preferred in childbirth, and sometimes special herbal preparations may be given to mothers during pregnancy, labour and after. A time of separation and purification may be observed after the birth.

Death Customs

Attendance at funerals is not of utmost importance as the beliefs and principles of Rastafarians celebrate life, rather than death.

Blood Transfusions and Transplants

May be refused – the patient should be consulted.

Family Planning

Contraception is often rejected, and birth control is managed through self-control.

National Contact

The Rastafarian Society
290-296 Tottenham High Road
London
N15 4AJ
Tel: 020 8808 2185

SIKHS

'There exists but one God, who is called the True, the Creator, free from fear and hate, immortal, not begotten, self-existent, great and compassionate.' (from Guru Nanak's hymn)

Estimated Community Size: Global 23,260,000 : UK 350,000 – 500,000

History, Beliefs and Principles

The Sikh religion was founded by Guru Nanak in Punjab in the sixteenth century. Sikhs come from the Indian region of Punjab. The UK Sikh community is the largest outside of India.

Born in Talvandi in 1469, Guru Nanak envisaged a society in which every member would work for the common good – the Sikh religion was based on certain features of Hinduism and Islam and emphasises the one-ness of God. He and the nine other Gurus (Gurus are religious leaders) who followed him over a period of 200 years sought to set an example in the way of living spiritually while at the same time taking an active part in the world. Guru Nanak was opposed to religious practices taking the form of superstitions, ritual acts and idol worship, which he saw as barriers rather than aids to worship. He spoke against the caste system, against customs of 'purdah' (veiling) and 'sati'. He stressed the virtues of truthfulness, kindness and generosity. The tenth Guru, Gobind Singh, moulded the Sikh community into a marshall nation with a common loyalty and a common purpose, and at the same time introduced a more democratic form of organisation with less reliance on a single man. He introduced Sikh baptism in 1699: all baptised adopted the same family names of 'Singh' (lion) for men and 'Kaur' (princess) for women, and the men and women all wore five symbols of brotherhood, the 5 'K's (see DRESS section below). The Guru also instructed the Sikhs to rise early and say prayers in the morning, at sunset and before returning to bed; to abstain from tobacco, drugs and alcohol; to refrain from adultery; and to contribute one-tenth of their income to religious purposes or for the needy in the community.

Religious Texts

The Sikh holy book is the Guru Granth Sahib

Religious Festivals

There are many Sikh festivals. The major ones are

Diwali (Festival of lights – Oct / Nov)
Baisakhi (First Day of the New Year - April)
Birth of Guru Gobind Singh (Birth of the tenth Guru – Jan / Feb)
Birth of Guru Nanak (Birth of the founder – Oct / Nov)

Predominant Languages

Punjabi is the main language of Sikhs (written form is called Gurmukhi), although the national language of India is Hindi. Younger Sikhs are likely to speak and write English fluently. Older generations may speak little or no English.

Worship

The Sikh temple is called the gurdwara, where the book of scriptures is kept with utmost respect. Before Guru Gobind Singh died he declared that the book of scriptures, 'Guru Granth Sahib', should be his successor; and it is through this holy book that Sikhs now approach the 'Waheguru', the Wonderful Lord. There are no priests in Sikhism; any competent person from the community can lead services. Sikhs pray in the morning and in the evening, and are also asked to recite hymns whenever they have time in the day. The gurdwara is open to all, regardless of race, religion or status.

Names

Sikhs have three names – a personal name, then a title (Singh for all men, Kaur for all women), then the family name eg Harbans Singh Gill, Davinder Kaur Bhuller. Sikhs usually prefer to be called by their first name, or by their first name and the honorific title. However to avoid confusion in the records it is best to obtain the family name if possible, and to use it thus: - Gill, H.S. (man); Bhuller D.K. (women). Explain why you want the family name for the written records.

Dress

Men's hair is kept long and is normally worn in a turban. They avoid shaving. The five K's are observed: kesh – uncut hair; kangha – the comb; kara – the steel bangle; kirpan – a short sword or dagger; and kachha – white shorts. These are sacred and should not be disturbed without consent or unless absolutely necessary.

Diet

Many Sikhs are vegetarian. Those Sikhs who eat meat only eat meat slaughtered according to their own rites – this is known as "jhatka". Sikhs do not eat beef or any meat that has been slaughtered according to Halal or Kosher rites. It is therefore essential to avoid contamination with beef or other meats at all stages of preparation, storage and serving.

Fasting

As a rule most Sikhs do not fast for religious reasons. However some Sikhs may wish to fast for personal or health reasons.

Birth Customs

Relatives will be anxious to visit the mother and child as soon as possible after the birth. This is a time of great rejoicing, with distribution of sweets to celebrate the occasion. Relatives will be anxious that the mother has complete rest for forty days after birth – they will be very worried if she has to get up for a bath within the first few days, for example. This attitude is based on the belief that a woman is at her weakest at this time and very susceptible to chills, backache, etc. On the other hand, it may require considerable tact and gentle persuasion to reconcile the mother to her baby being placed in a separate room, if the hospital's procedures require this. Visiting relatives will sometimes have to be persuaded to leave gifts of new clothing for the baby at the bedside, rather than putting them on straight away.

Death Customs

In the final stages of illness a Sikh patient will be comforted by reciting hymns from the holy book. A Granthi from the local temple or another practicing Sikh may do this with the patient. Sikhs, like Hindus, believe in the cycle of rebirth and reincarnation. The body is washed, and white clothes put on before cremation. Cremation should take place as soon as possible after death. Sikhs do not like the idea of a post-mortem, but will accept it if it is legally unavoidable.

Attitudes to Medical and Social Services Staff and Illness

Generally speaking, Sikh patients will be willing to accept the authority of the professional, whether male or female. They may tend to favour home remedies for ailments such as coughs, and be slow to seek professional attention.

Blood Transfusions and Transplants

Sikhs have no objection to these.

Family Planning

Sikhs have no objection to family planning.

Washing and Toilet

As with other Asian patients, Sikhs prefer to wash in free flowing water, rather than sitting in a bath; and they will appreciate having water provided in the same room as the W.C., or with a bedpan when one has to be used. They will want to wash their hands and rinse their mouth before meals.

Blood Transfusions and Transplants

Women prefer to be examined by female doctors, but in the case of emergencies they may not mind being examined by male doctors provided there is a female member of staff present. Likewise, they should be accommodated in mixed wards only in emergencies. Staff can help avoid embarrassment by being helpful and understanding – for example, when patient finds it difficult to accept an X-ray gown because of its shortness.

National Contact

Network of Sikh Organisations UK
1st Floor Office Suite
192 The Broadway
Wimbledon
London SW19 1RY
Tel: 020 8540 3974

ZOROASTRIANS

'Good thoughts. Good words. Good deeds.'
(Zoroastrian Declaration of Intention)
Estimated Community Size: Global 2,545,000 : UK 5,000 – 10,000

History, Beliefs and Principles

Zoroastrians are a long established community in the UK, settling in the UK in the 19th century. Other Zorastrians arrived in the 1950s after Indian Independence, from East Africa in the 1960s and 70s and from Iran in 1979 after the downfall of the Pahlavi dynasty. There has been significant migration - in the 10th century, a group settled in India and became known as Parsis. Today Zoroastrians live mainly in Iran, India (Bombay and Gujarat State), the UK, N America, Australia and New Zealand.

Zoroastrianism is the religion of Zoroaster, the Prophet of ancient Iran. It was the most influential religion in the Middle East at the time of the birth of Christianity. Its teaching can be epitomised as a conscious effort made by man who was given free will to choose from the eternal struggle between Good and Evil. Those choosing to follow the Book in their daily behaviour and action should live joyful and happy lives with no need to fast, practise celibacy or other means of atonement, and would attain salvation in Heaven.

Names

Every boy/girl, married man/woman has three names – Given name (forename), Father's forename (middle name) and Surname (family name, may indicate a profession). When a girl marries or re-marries, the middle name is changed to that of the husband.

Predominant Languages

The majority of the youth will be fluent in English.
Elderly generations may speak only Parsi Gujarati or Farsi (Persian)

Worship

Prayers are said in Pahlavi and Avesta – the languages of ancient Iran.

Traditionally Zoroastrian places of worship are known as Fire Temples as a fire burns perpetually inside. Fire is central to worship and has become an icon of Zoroastrianism and as such, Zoroastrians keep an oil lamp burning in their homes. However Zoroastrians do not worship fire – they worship Ahura Mazda. When preparing for prayer they will want to wash their face, hands and all uncovered parts of their bodies and facilities should be made available.

Religious Texts

The main body of Zoroastrian scripture is known as the Avesta and originally consisted of 21 books written in a specially composed Avestan alphabet.

Religious Festivals

Festivals are central to Zoroastrians life and they will wish to celebrate in hospital wherever possible. The main festivals are

Gahanbars (series of 6 seasonal festivals throughout the year, lasting for 5 days each)

No-Ruz (New Year's Day – Festival of the arrival of Spring, 20th / 21st March)

Khordad Sal (birth of Prophet Zarathustra, 6th day after No-Ruz)

Zarthosht no Diso (Death of Zarathushtra, 5th day 10th month)

Muktad (marks the final days of the year, 25th day, 12th month)

Diet

There is no religious restriction about diet or alcohol. By tradition, however, the orthodox do not eat beef or pork, and because of the religious exhortation to look to the interests of God's other creatures, orthodox Zoroastrians do not eat meat on certain days in a month nor in one whole particular month in a year.

Dress

At all times Zoroastrians should wear the sudreh and kushti. The sudereh is a sacred shirt, worn in white (to symbolize purity) and is made of muslin or cotton. The kushti is a sacred cord worn over the sudreh and is passed 3 times around the waist. Only with permission should these articles be removed.

Birth Customs

Today, one can only be a Zoroastrian by birth. All Zoroastrian / Parsi children are admitted into the faith at a ceremony a few years later called 'Navjote' (Parsi Gujarati) or Sedreh (Farsi), when the child has to wear a sacred white muslim undervest called Sudrah, on which is wound in three layers a sacred courd called Kusti, whilst chanting prayers. Zoroastrians are required to unwind and re-don the Kusti at least twice a day – in the morning and before retiring at night.

Death Customs

The Zoroastrian creed believes that the soul at death is earthbound for three days, so it is necessary to commence prayers as soon as possible after death the body may be buried as per family wishes but it is very important that the burial takes place within 24 hours. Post-mortem and donation of organs are not always acceptable

There is a problem if no other relative is available on the spot. In order to request that death ceremonies and prayers be commenced pending further instructions, if any, from any traceable next-of-kin, contact should be made at the address over the page. Both cremation and internment are acceptable forms of disposal. The full three names should be given for inclusion in the prayers – initials alone for the forename and father/husband's name are not sufficient.

Attitudes to Medical and Social Staff and Illness

Zoroastrians have had to be Westernised in their outlook since their small numbers could not sustain a totally separate way of life in the countries in which they have settled. Thus, their requirements relating washing and toilet etc should present no problem to hospital staff.

Blood Transfusions and Transplants

There should be no objection to blood transfusions and transplants

Family Planning

Zoroastrians have no religious restriction in this regard. Amongst Parsis there is a slight bias in favour of male children, however it should be noted that they were one of the first communities in India to give full opportunity to girls for education and careers.

Other Special Considerations

Proneness to Specific Illnesses

Due to the small number of the community in general, the selection of marriage partners is not as diverse as is desirable or possible in a larger group. Therefore, there is greater likelihood of conditions with hereditary aspects, such as Rh Negative blood group, G6 PD (another blood condition in which drugs like Aspirin are contraindicated), diabetes, cancer and coronary problems.

National Contacts

Zoroastrian Trust Funds of Europe
Zoroastrian House
88 Compayne Gardens
West Hampstead
London NW6 3RU
Tel: 020 7328 6018

World Zoroastrian Organisation
135 Tennison Rd
South Norwood
London
SE25 5NF
Tel: 020 8660 5048

AGNOSTICS, ATHEISTS, AND PEOPLE OF NO RELIGION

It should not be assumed that people who describe themselves as agnostics or people of no religion, have no belief, or that they wish to be ignored by Chaplains in hospital. They often use such terms to express that they do not belong to a form of organised religion. Many amongst these have lost faith in organised religious structures, or are suspicious of organised religions.

People are often glad of human support and friendship, including that offered by Chaplains, and sometimes a healing of hurts and a recovery of faith can take place. But any approach needs to be with much tact, sensitivity and compassion.

notes